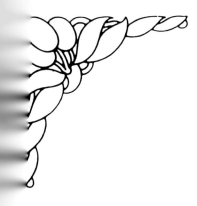

Melmac
Dinnerware

Wheeler Station
PO Box 83
Wheeler, OR 97147-0083

by

Gregory R. Zimmer & Alvin Daigle, Jr.

© 1997

Published by

L-W BOOK SALES
P.O. Box 69
Gas City, IN 46933

ISBN#: 0-89538-085-4

Published by: L-W BOOK SALES
                      P.O. Box 69
                      Gas City, IN 46933

Please write for our free catalog.

Printed by IMAGE GRAPHICS, INC., Paducah, Kentucky

Table of Contents

Acknowledgments

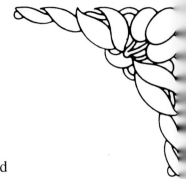

Many special thanks to the following:

Claire Ouellette for her patience, constant encouragement, and immeasurable assistance with both the photographic and textual aspects of the book.

Alan Kohl for his photographic assistance.

David Anderson for the many original brochures and advertisements.

Family, friends, and co-workers who gave added information and numerous gifts of plastic dinnerware.

Pricing Information

The values in this book should be used only as a guide. These prices will vary from one section of the country to the other. All prices are also affected by the condition as well as the demand of the piece.

Neither the Author nor the Publisher assumes responsibility for any gains or losses that might be incurred as a result of using this guide.

Collectors Guide to Plastic Dinnerware

The basic purpose of this book is to identify the different makes of plastic dinnerware, also called melamine dinnerware and sometimes generically referred to as Melmac. Identification is based on the different brand names, their manufacturers, designers involved, dates of manufacturing, markings (embossed on the underside of the pieces), or other identifying stamps, colors, discussion of styles and shapes, and information from advertisements, packaging, or labels.

All of this is a result of our own collecting and research. The items presented here are from one collection now in excess of 3500 pieces. Plastic dinnerware is a vast area of collecting, and although items from several foreign countries are included in the collection, all the pieces represented here are American (U.S.A.) made plastic dinnerware.

Our effort is aimed at providing a general guide to plastic dinnerware manufacturers rather than a comprehensive list of plastic dinnerware manufacturers. This guide is, therefore, representative of the types of plastic dinnerware which comprise our collection.

The general terms used herein to describe the weight and thickness of the various plastic dinnerware lines are heavyweight (thick-walled, solid, weighty), medium-weight (less thick-walled, average weight), and lightweight (thin-walled, slight, having little weight). Pattern names are provided only when the proper name is known.

For reference only

Background

From the Latin *plasticus* and the Greek *plastikos*, both which mean "that which may be molded" we have the noun *"plastic"*: any of a group of synthetic or natural organic materials which may be shaped when soft and then hardened.

The materials used in plastic dinnerware manufacturing presented here are known as thermosetting plastics. The most generally used thermosetting materials for molded dinnerware were melamine resins which are formed by the interaction of melamine and formaldehyde.

Thermosetting plastics first become soft by heating, then are permanently hardened or set by a chemical change when the heating process is continued; subsequently they cannot be remolded or melted down to their original resinous state. Melamine resin's resistance to heat and other chemicals, its tough, hard surface, its wide range of colors, and its durability made it particularly suitable for use in molded dinnerware. This dinnerware could easily be formed into a variety of shapes and brilliant colors with lustrous surfaces characteristic of modern age machine production.

Thermosetting plastics were fabricated into dinnerware by a production process called compression molding. The granular molding compound is placed in a heated mold, put under pressure and left in the hot mold until the material is set. Removed while still hot, the finished product is produced. Flowing, smooth lines became characteristic of plastic dinnerware and their methods of manufacture. Compression mold lines, known as flash lines, were hidden and spurs removed by machining, thus plastic dinnerware pieces could be uniformly produced with repeated accuracy and perfection of shape.

Plastic dinnerware was readily and economically reproduced, thus it became increasingly popular for mass use in restaurants, cafeterias, hospitals, and other institutional settings. This trend met resistance from chinaware manufacturers trying to protect their market. In response, standards and specifications for melamine dinnerware were instituted in 1950 with the cooperation of the Society for the Plastics Industry and the U.S. Bureau of Standards. These standards governed matters of size, weight, density, sanitation, and even the surface or tactile qualities of molded items. Industrial designers used these standards as guidelines in their design processes dealing with new materials and molding methods used with plastic dinnerware. Occasionally plastic dinnerware pieces display a symbol showing that the piece meets these standards.

Melamine dinnerware worked well in institutional situations because it was durable, easy to handle, could be stacked and stored, and withstood repeated machine washing and drying. Following plastic dinnerware's success in the institutional and utilitarian field, plastic dinnerware manufacturers shifted their focus toward making their products useful for everyday domestic household settings. However, what was acceptable in a dining hall wasn't necessarily suitable for the family dinner table. Questions arose concerning plastic dinnerware's sanitation because plastic was vulnerable to scratches, stains and burns. Therefore, manufacturers developed methods to make melamine dinnerware better resistant to heat, staining, color fading and abrasion.

With the advent of modernity in the 1950s, plastic became the material which could best meet the needs of postwar American families. These young families had a relaxed life-style, limited budgets, and domestic life centered around their children. Informal living and informal entertaining were the order of the day.

Everyone could afford stylish and functional plastic dinnerware products. These products were colorful, sturdy, basically resistant to breakage and wear; thus were childproof, carefree, inexpensive and affordable. Glamour had come to the utilitarian image of plastic as well. Flowing, organic forms, sleek lines, and glossy finishes brought a sense of order and cleanliness to the home. These qualities led to melamine dinnerware's suitability as everyday household dinnerware. Melamine dinnerware in the domestic market became one of plastic's greatest successes. The mix of good design plus practicality and a good price equalled the 1950s American dream of mass produced luxury.

After World War II American Cyanamid Corporation set about finding a domestic market for its melamine. The American Cyanamid trade name for its melamine products became known as Melmac. Although melamine dinnerware was not inexpensive when compared to some chinaware sets during the early 1950s, its durability and longevity made it a good consumer choice. The immediate investment in a good set of melamine dinnerware outweighed the long term costs of replacing broken pieces of chinaware. Advertising and packaging made plastic dinnerware seem more appealing and convenient to consumers. "Starter" sets, sample sets and larger complete dinnerware sets were offered in compact packaging that could serve as display units, carrying cases or storage units. Discount chain stores and supermarket promotions further broadened the public's awareness of plastic dinnerware.

Eventually plastic dinnerware began to lose its popular appeal when many of its acclaimed qualities gave way to its weaknesses. Over time, repeated washing, scrubbing and scouring caused some plastic dinnerware to become dull and faded. Edges could sometimes chip, surfaces were scratched and cut by metal knives, and cups were stained by coffee, tea and juices. Pieces could be damaged by stove heat, and burns or scars could result from placing plastic dinnerware in the oven to reheat food. Further, the early 1960s dinnerware designs became exaggerated: delicate, thin-walled, impractical, and essentially less substantial, these newer products abandoned the basic tenets of durability and unbreakability that were characteristic of 1950s plastic dinnerware. Plastic dinnerware began to imitate other materials rather than staying with its unique properties. Trends toward decorated lines with decal designs hastened its decline. By mimicking chinaware instead of staying with its original assets plastic dinnerware fell from household use. When a new wave of imported china and porcelain came to the United States from Asian and European markets in the late 1960s and early 1970s, plastic dinnerware could no longer compete in the American marketplace. The era of modern plastic dinnerware use came to a close as traditional materials for dinnerware products returned.

ABC

ABC was a medium to heavyweight dinnerware, made by ABC Manufacturing Company, Washington, D.C., and appears to have been used for institutional or commercial settings. The cups have exterior side bumps to facilitate uniform stacking, and in addition, footed bottoms for water drainage while washing, as do the plates and bowls.

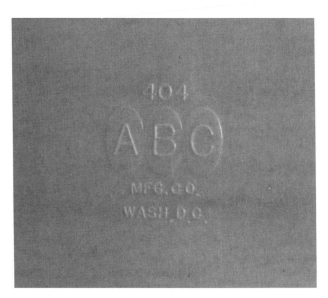

ABC Trademark

Salad plate, soup bowl and cups

Air Flite

Air Flite was manufactured by Plastics Incorporated, St. Paul, Minnesota and included plastic dinnerware made for commercial airlines: for example, Eastern, Continental, and BWIA. Plastics Incorporated also produced the Flite Lane dinnerware line.

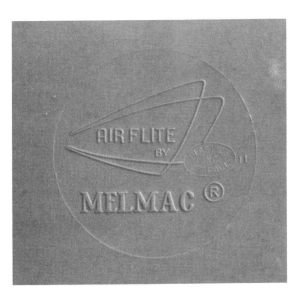

Air Flite Trademark

Salad plate and cup.

Apollo Ware

Apollo Ware was a medium-weight dinnerware line produced by Metro Molding Corporation, Cleveland, Ohio. Alexander Barna was a designer associated with Apollo Ware.

Apollo Ware Trademark

Serving bowls

Aztec

Aztec, of St. Louis, Missouri is a medium-weight dinnerware line featuring stackable, low, flat plates with high edges, as well as low bowls and serving pieces. The platter has rounded wing handles, as does the covered sugar bowl.

There are two main color groups: one is an opaque group of gray, mustard yellow, turquoise, and salmon-pink; the other is a pastel group of blue, pink, yellow, and white. A beige floral patterned set was also produced. One of the notable service pieces is the open-handled salad bowl.

Aztec Trademark

Dinner plate, salad plate, dessert bowl,
cup and saucer, and soup bowl

Platter, divided serving bowl,
covered sugar bowl and creamer.

Two-handled salad bowl.

Salad plate and cups.

Dinner plate, salad plate,
cup and saucer, and soup bowl.

Platter, serving bowl, covered sugar bowl and creamer

Aztec Dinnerware continued . . .

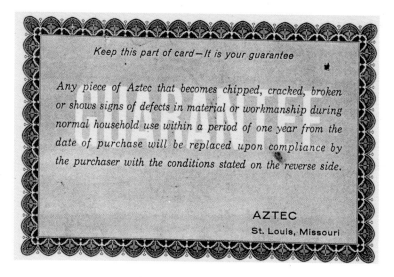

Keep this part of card—It is your guarantee

Any piece of Aztec that becomes chipped, cracked, broken or shows signs of defects in material or workmanship during normal household use within a period of one year from the date of purchase will be replaced upon compliance by the purchaser with the conditions stated on the reverse side.

AZTEC
St. Louis, Missouri

Tear off this reply card

IMPORTANT — Fill in information below and on reverse side. Mail this card now so that our records can be set up to honor your guarantee.

Your Name:.. Date of Purchase:...................
                Please Print   Date-Month-Year

Address:..
             Street   City   State

Store Name:...

Address:...
             Street   City

Was this set received as a gift? ☐ Yes ☐ No

FORM A3 PRINTED IN U.S.A.

CARE OF YOUR AZTEC

Aztec is a quality product that will give you years of carefree service. With normal care it is unbelievably resistant to damage.

Aztec can be washed by hand or in an automatic dishwasher, using standard soaps or detergents, in hot water. Should discoloration occur from tea or coffee left in cups, rub briskly with soap and towel-dry or use one of these special cleaning agents: "Reen'o Melmac Cleaner," "M-E Cleaner" or "Dip-It."

This guarantee is valid only on compliance with the following conditions:

1. The purchaser must complete the attached card and mail it within 10 days from the date of purchase, postage prepaid, to Aztec, Oleatha Avenue, St. Louis 16, Mo

2. Each damaged piece and this guarantee, together with the purchaser's name and address, must be forwarded to Aztec, Oleatha Avenue, St. Louis 16, Mo., together with 25¢ for each piece to cover postage and handling. You will receive a new article for each damaged article covered by this guarantee together with your guarantee by return mail.

3. This guarantee is void if any piece is purposely abused or if steel wool, scouring compounds or abrasives are used, or if Aztec is used for cooking, baking or over an open flame.

Be sure to fill in the information below for your own records.

Date of Purchase.. Store Name.......................................
                   Date - Month - Year

This guarantee is valid for 1 year from date of purchase.

Place
Stamp
Here

Aztec Dinnerware enclosure
card, front and back view.

AZTEC

4417 OLEATHA AVE.

ST. LOUIS 16, MO.

Boonton

Boonton is a heavyweight dinnerware line from the Boonton Molding Company, Boonton, New Jersey. The original Boonton and Boontonware commercial line appeared in 1948. Notable are the winged handles on the bowls, and stylish knob-handles on accessory pieces.

It came in manufacturer's colors such as: golden yellow, sea foam green, stone gray, forest green, cranberry red, powder blue, and tawny buff, charcoal gray, beige, pink, white, yellow, light green and turquoise. A 1953 Montgomery Ward catalog listed the following available pieces: dinner plate, salad-dessert plate, bread and butter plate, cup, saucer, vegetable-cereal dish, soup-salad dish, covered sugar bowl, creamer, vegetable or salad bowl, platter, and covered divided vegetable bowl.

Later Boontonware pieces are lighter in weight than earlier Boonton pieces. Belle Kogan Associates had worked with Bonton since 1951 on dinnerware design. In 1953-54 Belle Kogan designed a new line called Boonton Belle, which featured pieces with a trim, and circle shape. Manufacturer's colors were shrimp pink, turquoise blue, and oyster white. Additional colors were pewter gray, and charcoal. In 1957 Belle Kogan designed the Patrician (Crown Patrician) line of dinnerware for Boonton. There were both solid colors and four patterns available. The Patrician pieces were referred to as the coupe shape (basically rimless plates), with tapered lines, thin beveled edges, and footed bottoms. Another Boonton line was called Somerset.

Unusual Boonton pieces include nesting mixing bowls with fluted edges, a winged oval snack tray with a fitted holding place for a cup, covered divided serving bowls in speckled colors, oblong serving bowls, slim, beveled salt and pepper shakers, and a variety of creamers and lidded sugar bowls with both standard finger hole handles, and solid shaped handles.

Boonton Trademarks

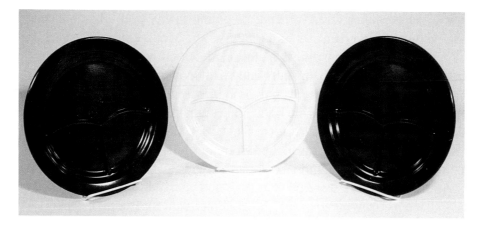

Divided dinner plates.

Plates, a bowl, and a cup and saucer.

Bowls

Serving/mixing bowls.

Covered sugar bowls, and creamers.

Creamers, covered sugar bowls,
(one creamer shown with sugar bowl lid as saucer).

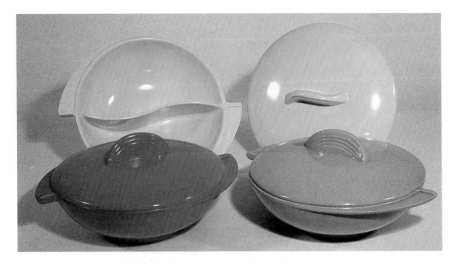

Divided serving bowls with covers.

Oval snack trays with cups.

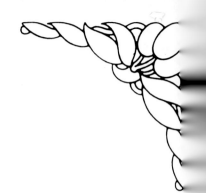

Boontonware

Boontonware Trademark

Boontonware Belle Trademark

Boontonware Ad from a May 1954 Catalog.

Boontonware continued . . .

Boontonware Ad

Oblong serving dish, salt and pepper,
covered sugar bowl and a creamer.

Bowls and a cup and saucer.

Oblong serving dish, covered sugar bowl and creamer.
(*The sugar bowl has a hole in the lid for a utensil*)

Plate and cups

Branchell

Branchell of St. Louis, Missouri produced a general line of medium-weight dinnerware, and two named lines, Color-Flyte and Royale. Identifying features include its mottled coloring, lug-handled bowls, and conical handled creamers and sugar bowls. Manufacturer's colors were mist grey, glade green, glow copper, and spray lime. Additional colors include red, turquoise, charcoal, and white (soft ivory).

Kaye LaMoyne was a dinnerware designer/stylist for Branchell. There were solid color and patterned lines available. Some patterned style names were Golden Harvest, Lady Fair, Tip Top, Sweet Talk, Rosedale, and Golden Grapes.

Unusual Branchell items include a pair of salad servers, an open-handled salad bowl, and large and small tumblers. From a 1956-57 merchandise catalog it appears that Color-Flyte flatware was also available.

A special item from the collection is an unused 53 piece service set for eight in the original manufacturer's box. The pattern is Sweet Talk, and the postage markings are from 1959. (November 27, 1959: possibly a Christmas present?)

Branchell Trademarks.

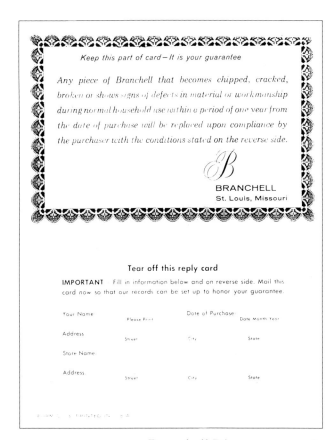

Keep this part of card – It is your guarantee

Any piece of Branchell that becomes chipped, cracked, broken or shows signs of defects in material or workmanship during normal household use within a period of one year from the date of purchase will be replaced upon compliance by the purchaser with the conditions stated on the reverse side.

B

BRANCHELL
St. Louis, Missouri

Tear off this reply card

IMPORTANT Fill in information below and on reverse side. Mail this card now so that our records can be set up to honor your guarantee.

Your Name _____
Please Print

Date of Purchase:
_____
Date Month Year

Address _____
Street   City   State

Store Name _____

Address _____
Street   City   State

CARE OF YOUR BRANCHELL

Branchell is a quality product that will give you years of carefree service. With normal care it is unbelievably resistant to damage.

Branchell can be washed by hand or in an automatic dishwasher, using standard soaps or detergents, in hot water. Should discoloration occur from tea or coffee left in cups, rub briskly with soap and towel-dry or use one of these special cleaning agents: "Reen'o Melmac Cleaner," "M-E Cleaner" or "DIP-IT."

This guarantee is valid only on compliance with the following conditions:

1. The purchaser must complete the attached card and mail it within 10 days from the date of purchase, postage prepaid, to Branchell, Oleatha Avenue, St. Louis 16, Mo.

2. Each damaged piece and this guarantee, together with the purchaser's name and address, must be forwarded to Branchell, Oleatha Avenue, St. Louis 16, Mo., together with 25¢ for each piece to cover postage and handling. You will receive a new article for each damaged article covered by this guarantee together with your guarantee by return mail.

3. This guarantee is void if any piece is purposely abused or if steel wool, scouring compounds or abrasives are used, or if Branchell is used for cooking, baking or over an open flame.

Be sure to fill in the information below for your own records.

Date of Purchase .... Store Name ....
Date · Month · Year

This guarantee is valid for 1 year from date of purchase.

Place
Stamp
Here

BRANCHELL
OLEATHA AVENUE
ST. LOUIS 16, MO.

Branchell Dinnerware enclosure card, front and back view.

Branchell continued . . .

MAIL ORDER FORM • CHECK PATTERNS DESIRED:

☐ TIP TOP   ☐ SWEET TALK   ☐ ROSEDALE

Code No.	Quantity	Retail Price	Open Stock Value
1120	20-Pc Set	$16.95	$ 37.80
1153	53-Pc Set	$39.95	$ 97.60

Code No.		Quantity	Price
11C	*Dinner Plate		$3.25
11E	*Salad Plate		2.75
11D	*Bread/Butter Plate		1.95
11B	*Saucer		1.85
11Q	*Platter		5.25
11A	Cup		1.10
11F	Fruit Dish		1.15
11H	Soup Bowl		1.30
11J	Tumbler, large		1.25
11K	Sugar w/lid		2.50
11M	Creamer		1.80
11O	Open Veg. Bowl		3.25
11SP	Salt & Pepper		2.15

*Decorated all others white

Charge ___   Check or M.O. Enclosed ___

Name _____

Address _____

City _____ Zone _____ State _____

BRANCHELL
Quality Melamine Dinnerware

CANDLELIGHT BUFFET THIS EVENING

FAMILY BREAKFAST TOMORROW

PATIO PARTY THIS WEEKEND!

Beautiful and break-resistant a tribute to any table . . . in three lovely Lenox Plastics patterns

BRANCHELL

ROSEDALE
Like rambler roses on a garden wall . . . pink blossoms, buds and tiny green leaves form a dainty garland nestled on pure white.

TIP TOP
A charming French Provencial motif with delicate spring tracery gives this pattern the grace and joy of springtime. Soft, Bermuda blue against delicate white.

SWEET TALK
Fresh beauty and subtle simplicity, in a dainty spring garden design! Bermuda blue, coral and beige blossoms on a glowing white background.

53-Pc Service for 8 $39.95
(25 Decorated*)   Open Stock Value $97.60

8 each: Dinner Plates*, Bread/Butter Plates*, Saucers*, Cups, Soup Bowls, Fruit Dishes, and 1 each: Platter*, Creamer, Sugar w/lid, Open Veg. Bowl.

20-Pc Service for 4 $16.95
(12 Decorated*)   Open Stock Value $37.80

4 each: Dinner Plates*, Bread/Butter Plates*, Saucers*, Cups, Soup Bowls.

The look of elegance

GOLDEN HARVEST

Delicate, gleaming golden and white accents against a soft ivory background. Never before such glowing beauty in break-resistant dinnerware. Every piece styled to set a gracious mood for every meal.

GOLDEN GRAPES

The glitter of gold, on delicate grapes. And daintily sprinkled on cool green leaves. A vineyard in bloom, against the softness of ivory. Gracefully styled for everyday living or formal occasion.

. . . BRANCHELL

Deluxe

16-Pc Service for 4 $19.95
(8 Decorated*)   Open Stock Value $31.00
4 each: Dinner Plates*, Saucers*, Cups, Fruit Dishes.

45-Pc Service for 8 $49.95
(25 Decorated*)   Open Stock Value $105.70

8 each: Dinner Plates*, Salad Plates*, Saucers*, Cups, Soup Bowls, and 1 each: Platter*, Creamer, Sugar w/lid, Divided Vegetable Bowl.

79-Pc Service for 12 $79.95
(38 Decorated*)   Open Stock Value $173.00

12 each: Dinner Plates*, Salad Plates*, Saucers*, Cups, Soup Bowls, Fruit Dishes, 2 Platters*, and 1 each: Creamer, Sugar w/lid, Divided Vegetable Bowl, Open Vegetable Bowl.

Two lovely and lasting gold patterns in break-resistant quality Melamine by LENOX PLASTICS

MAIL ORDER FORM • CHECK PATTERNS DESIRED

☐ GOLDEN HARVEST   ☐ GOLDEN GRAPES

Code No.	Quantity	Retail Price	Open Stock Value
216A	16-Pc Set	$19.95	$ 31.00
245S	45-Pc Set	$49.95	$105.70
279	79-Pc Set	$79.95	$173.00

Code No.		Quantity	Price
2C	*Dinner Plate		$3.25
2E	*Salad Plate		2.75
2A	Cup		1.50
2B	*Saucer		1.85
2F	Fruit Dish		1.15
2N	Soup Bowl		1.90
2J	Tumbler, large		1.25
2Q	*Platter		5.25
2K	Sugar w/lid		3.25
2M	Creamer		2.25
2O	Open Veg. Bowl		3.25
2P	Div. Veg. Bowl		4.95

*Decorated all others soft ivory

FULLY GUARANTEED FOR ONE FULL YEAR!
Pieces replaced free by LENOX PLASTICS.
Postage and handling charge, 25¢.

Charge ☐   Check or M.O. Enclosed ☐

Name _____

Address _____

City _____ Zone _____ State _____

Branchell Pamphlets

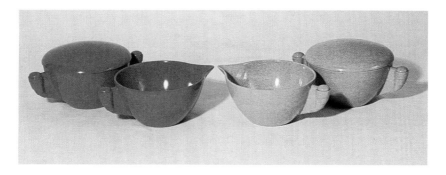

Covered sugar bowls with creamers

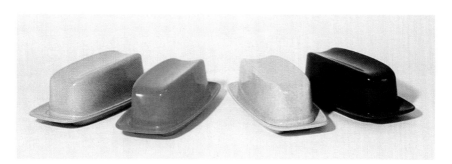

Covered butter dishes

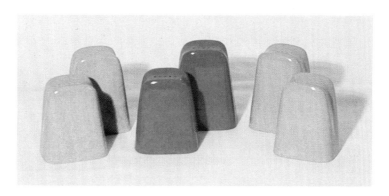

Salt and peppers

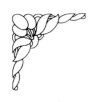

Small tumblers

Gravy boats, creamer, and covered sugar bowl

Platter, covered butter dish,
covered sugar bowl and a creamer

Bowl, serving bowl, covered
sugar bowl, and creamer

Platter and dinner plate

Platter, open vegetable bowl, covered sugar bowl,
and creamer, "Sweet Talk" pattern

Original box for set of dinnerware, "Sweet Talk" pattern

Dinner plate, bread and butter plate, soup bowl,
cup and saucer, and fruit dish, "Sweet Talk" pattern

Original box for set of dinnerware,
"Sweet Talk" pattern

Branchell Color-Flyte Trademark

Serving bowl, salad servers,
salt and pepper, and gravy boat

Platters, covered butter dish,
divided serving bowl,
creamer, and covered sugar bowl

Dinner plate, salad plate, bread
and butter plate, dessert bowl, small
tumbler, cup and saucer, and soup bowl

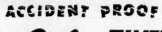

ACCIDENT PROOF

Color-FLYTE

the Gre...
in Melmac Di......are

STYLE

Modern...smart...practical...
"Accident-Proof" Color-Flyte is
designed with the accent on style.
Its modern simplicity and decorator
colors reflect good taste...
at breakfast, lunch, dinner, parties,
buffets . truly 'round-the-clock
dinnerware.

COLOR

Color-Flyte is bright and cheery.
Its softly-mottled undertones accent
color richness...makes table settings
more attractive. Color-Flyte can
be used in sets of one color...or the
four colors, Grey, Green, Copper and
Lime, can be mixed to please
individual tastes.

DURABILITY

A set of Color-Flyte will always be
complete...no cups without handles
...no cracked pieces to mar the
original beauty. Color-Flyte is
"Accident-Proof"...Guaranteed for one
full year against chipping, cracking
or breaking, in normal household use.
It can be washed in automatic
dishwasher and rinsed in boiling water
...without damage to color or surface.

16-Piece Starter Set

4—10" Dinner Plates
4—Bread and Butter
    Plates
4—Cups
4—Saucers

$15.95

47-Piece Service for Eight

8—8-oz. cups
8—Saucers
8—6" Bread and Butter
    Plates
8—10" Dinner Plates
8—Lug Soup/Cereal

1—Creamer
1—Sugar with Lid (2 pcs.)
1—Platter
1—10" Vegetable Bowl
1—Pair Servers (2 pcs.)

$54.95

OPEN STOCK AVAILABLE

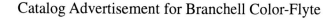

Catalog Advertisement for Branchell Color-Flyte

Branchell continued . . .

At last!

No More Broken Dishes

with ACCIDENT PROOF

Color-FLYTE
Dinnerware

Guaranteed by Good Housekeeping

▶ **GUARANTEED**
for ONE full year ◀

A slip . . . a spill . . . another costly dinnerware accident. But not with "Accident Proof" Color-Flyte. After years of every day use colors stay cheery . . . sets stay complete. And boiling water never affects it. See, feel, and drop Color-Flyte—you'll be amazed . . . and convinced.

16 PIECE STARTER SET

Contains four large 10" plates, four 8 oz. cups, four saucers, and four bread and butter plates. **$14⁹⁵**

OPEN STOCK AVAILABLE
Grey • Green • Copper • Lime

FREE! Write for color catalog

THE BRANCHELL COMPANY
2695 Twentieth Ave. • San Francisco 16, Calif.

104

ACCIDENT PROOF
Color-FLYTE
DINNERWARE
by *BRANCHELL*

So Modern . . .
So Colorful . . .
So Versatile . . .

ACCIDENT PROOF

Melmac
DINNERWARE

Color-Flyte is the perfect answer to modern day tastes and modern day living. Sleek and streamlined in a luscious array of colors . . . Color-Flyte will cheer up your meals, any meal, and win you a host of compliments.

Think of the convenience and economy of *always* having a *complete* set of dinnerware . . . Color-Flyte is guaranteed not to chip, crack or break for one full year . . . not affected by boiling water or repeated washing in mechanical dishwashers.

16 Piece Starter Set	35 Piece Service for 6	47 Piece Service for 8
$15.95	**$39.95**	**$54.95**

In Mist Grey, Glade Green, Glow Copper, Spray Lime or assorted rainbow pack.
Open stock available at major department and neighborhood stores.

Write for free color catalog

THE BRANCHELL CO.
1075 Golden Gate Ave.   San Francisco, Calif.

81

Ad for Color-Flyte
Dinnerware by Branchell

Ad for Color-Flyte
Dinnerware by Branchell

Branchell Royale

Branchell Color-Flyte
Royale Trademark

Branchell Royale Trademark

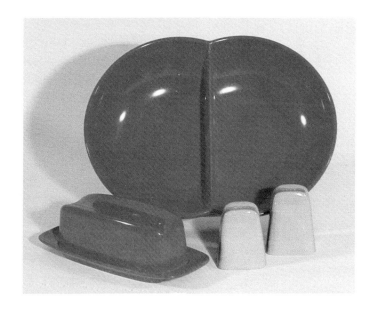

Divided serving bowl, covered
butter dish, and salt and pepper

Dinner plates, cups,
and small tumbler

Brookpark

Brookpark was manufactured by International Molded Products in Cleveland, Ohio. Brookpark Arrowhead Ever Ware was designed by Joan Luntz in 1950 and included items featuring the round-corner square shape. This line of dinnerware won a Good Design Award from the Museum of Modern Art (New York, N.Y.) The Arrowhead Ever Ware and Efficiency Ware lines were also produced in the standard round shape, and included a three-part divided dinner plate.

Brookpark Modern Design was also designed by Joan Luntz and won a Good Design Award from the Museum of Modern Art (New York, N.Y.) The main identifying feature of this line was the round-corner square shape of its pieces. Manufacturer's colors were chartreuse, burgundy, emerald, and pearl gray. Additional manufacturer's colors included turquoise, white, pink, black, yellow, and stone. Colors were also available in combinations: white and turquoise, yellow and black, stone and turquoise, and pink and black. Another feature included handles on the diagonal corners of the sugar bowl, and flat, tab-handles on the regular bowls.

Unusual pieces in the Modern Design line are the two and three tier tidbit tray, salt and pepper shakers, and a gravy boat. The round shaped Brookpark Desert Flower line designed by Joan Luntz in 1951 featured an incised floral pattern into the plates and cups. Manufacturer's colors included slate blue, navajo brown, pebble gray, canyon gold, dawn pink, and sage green. It was also available in black, turquoise, and white.

Brookpark introduced the first patterned melamine dinnerware in 1956 with the Fantasy line. Brookpark produced many additional patterned lines including: Delicado, Pink Hyacinth, Tropicana, Only a Rose, Bluebells, Golden Pine, Gaiety, Contemporary, Dual-Tone, Magic Carpet, Elegance, Pavillion, and Flower Box.

 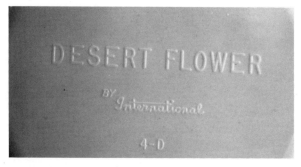

Brookpark Trademarks

Brookpark Modern Design by Joan Luntz
Brochure on dinnerware

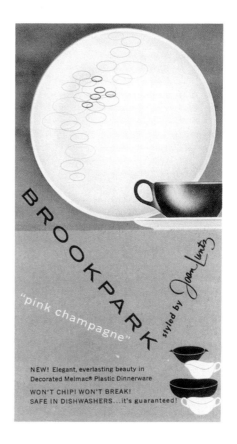

Brookpark Dinnerware Brochures

May 1955 Ad for Brookpark Dinnerware

April 20, 1949 Life Magazine Ad

Dinner plates with cups and saucers,
"Desert Flower" design

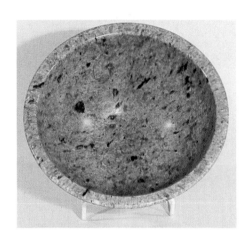

Serving bowl

Plate, "Desert Flower" design

Serving bowl

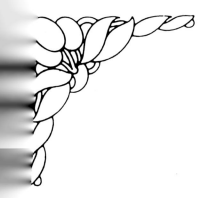

Brookpark Arrowhead

Brookpark Arrowhead Trademark

Divided dinner plates

Plate, bowl and two cups

Brookpark Arrowhead Ever Ware

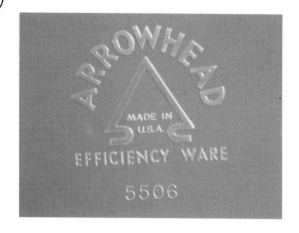

Brookpark Arrowhead
Efficiency Ware Trademark

Brookpark Arrowhead
Ever Ware Trademark

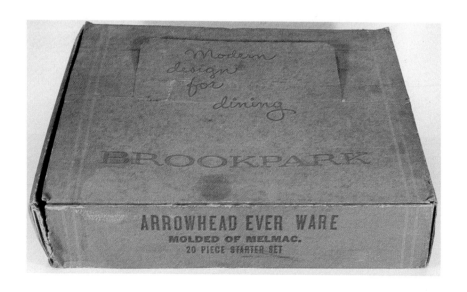

Original box for a
20 piece dinnerware set

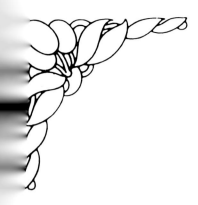

Brookpark Modern Design

Brookpark Modern Design Trademark

Brookpark Tropicana Trademark

Brookpark Town and Country Trademark

Stack of cups and saucers

Covered sugar bowl and creamer

Salad plate, dinner plate, dessert
bowl, cup and saucer, and soup bowl

Two creamers and
a handleless cup

Salad plate, dinner plate, dessert
bowl, and cup and saucer,
"Tropicana" pattern

Serving dish, covered sugar bowl,
creamer, and covered butter dish,
"Tropicana" pattern

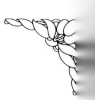

Brookpark Modern Design continued . . .

Covered sugar bowls,
and creamer

A bowl and cups and saucers

Platter, serving dish, and a
divided serving dish

Debonaire (by Kenro)

Debonaire is a medium-weight dinnerware line produced by Kenro Company, Fredonia, Wisconsin, the maker of Holiday dinnerware, and other lines as well.

Debonaire's design features trim lines and a sleek look, both in solid colors and flecked colors of pink, white, turquoise, yellow, and a rust red.

Debonaire Trademark

Dinner plate and bowls

Covered sugar bowls
and a creamer

Devine Ware

Jim Devine of Devine Foods, Incorporated, Chicago, Illinois was a pioneer in the use of melamine and developed a line of dinnerware for institutional use, utilizing plastic similar to the kind used for making military food trays.

His designs had some innovative and unique features: there was a notched foot on plates, cups, and bowls to prevent a vacuum from forming between stacked pieces; a small lip molded into the side of cups made for uniform stacking and good air circulation for drying. In addition he developed a cup whose bottom was indented and fit onto a saucer with a raised middle, allowing less slippage to occur. Later the Florence line designed by Irving Harper for Prolon would use this feature.

NOTE:

No photo available – No trademarks available.

Durawear

Durawear was a medium-weight dinnerware made by California Molded Products, Incorporated, Santa Paula, California.

The basic shape featured a low, trim look and colors included red, yellow, pink, turquoise, and brown. One patterned line was named Caribe.

Durawear Trademark

Elan

Elan is a medium-weight dinnerware line manufactured by Plastics Manufacturing Company, Dallas, Texas, the same company that produces Texas Ware, and Dallas Ware.

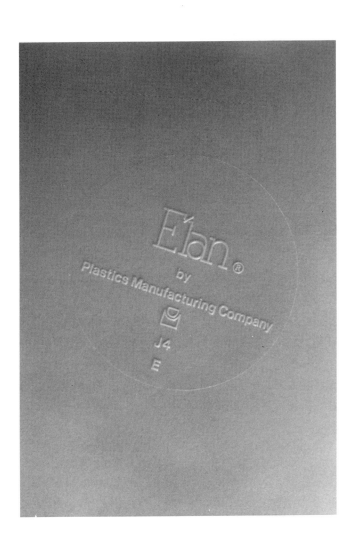

Elan Trademark

Flite Lane

Flite Lane is a medium to lightweight dinnerware line manufactured by Plastics Incorporated, St. Paul, Minnesota. It's general appearance would indicate a more institutional than domestic use. The colors are mottled with brown flecks, and colors include turquoise, yellow, brown, and a red-orange (with yellow flecks).

Flite Lane Trademark

Dinner plate, salad plate, bread and butter plate, dessert bowl, soup bowl, and cup and saucer

Small and large tumblers

Platter and serving bowl

Fostoria

Fostoria melamine dinnerware was made by the Fostoria Glass Company, Moundsville, West Virginia, known makers of quality glassware.

Latham-Tyler-Jensen, designers from Chicago, worked with Fostoria design director Martin Yutzey and Chicago Molded Products to produce their first line. Notable in their design was the beveled edge and two-tone designs of the plates, and the cups' noticeably rising handle.

Manufacturer's colors were sky blue, fawn (beige), harvest yellow, and white. An additional color was a light green.

Patterns included Blue Meadow, Ring O' Roses, Kismet, Casual Flair, Plain N' Fancy, Country Garden, and Golden Twilight.

A notable piece in this line is the oval three-part serving dish. One of the more desirable service pieces would be the pitcher.

Advertisement for Fostoria Dinnerware

51

Fostoria continued . . .

Fostoria Trademark

Covered butter dish, covered
sugar bowl, and creamer

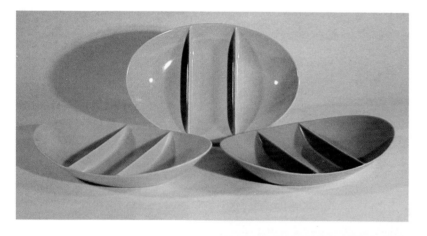

Divided serving bowls

Platter, serving bowl, and
a divided serving bowl

Harmony House

Harmony House was a heavyweight dinnerware manufactured by Plastic Masters, New Buffalo, Michigan, and was available through Sears and Roebuck Company.

In 1953 Sears and Roebuck introduced the Talk of the Town melamine line. The design featured square pieces with rounded corners and beveled edges, and cups with accented angular handles. Manufacturer's colors were chartreuse, dawn grey, Victorian red, and mint green. The Today line was introduced by Harmony House in 1954, in the standard round shape, and was available in original colors of spice beige, aquamarine, sunshine yellow, and dawn grey.

In 1955 Talk of the Town was renamed New Talk of the Town and additional manufacturer's colors available were frosty pink, medium federal gold, clay beige, and medium sage green.

Also in 1955 a new line, Catalina, was introduced featuring a squared design, with the coupe, or rimless, plate. Original manufacturer's colors were Inca gold, Malibu coral, spice beige, and bronze green. Catalina translucent came out in 1957, available in Ming blue, light federal gold, parchment beige, and light Malibu coral.

Additional Harmony House solid color dinnerware lines included Avalon, Windsor (introduced in 1959 in blue, pink, yellow, and ivory), and Easy Livin' (introduced in 1961 in turquoise, pink, yellow, and ivory).

From 1957 on Harmony House patterned lines included Floral Lace, Mademoiselle, Province, Crocus, Frolic, Patio Rose, Autumn Leaves, and Golden Spears.

Harmony House
"Catalina" Trademark

Harmony House
"Today" Trademark

Harmony House
"Talk of the Town"
Trademark

Cups and saucers

Covered sugar bowl and creamer

Cups and saucers

Dinner plate, salad plate,
and cup and saucer

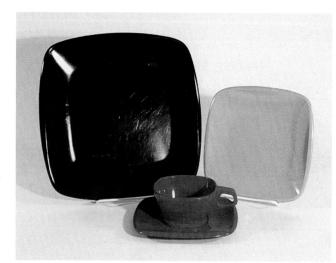

Platter, "Autumn Leaves" pattern,
and plate

Dinner plate, salad plate,
cup and saucer and creamer

Three bowls and a cup

Serving dish, covered sugar bowl and creamer

Holiday (by Kenro)

Holiday, a medium-weight dinnerware line, was manufactured by Kenro Company, Fredonia, Wisconsin.

Holiday's identifying features include its low-slung, flared shape with downward swooping handles on the cups, and its speckled colors which came in red, blue, turquoise, pink, yellow, and white. Some of Holiday's patterned lines were Orchid Spray, Seneca, and Gale Art.

An unusual accessory item to look for is the three-part ice bucket.

A unique item from the collection is a special set of checkered black and white "op art" patterned tableware designed by Tom Strobel for Holiday. The markings on the plates refer to the set as signature multiples and a limited edition.

Holiday Trademarks

Three-part ice bucket
(assembled).

Three-part ice bucket
(disassembled to show all the pieces).

A serving bowl, and a divided serving bowl.

Platter, creamers, covered sugar bowls.

Dinner plate, bread and butter plate, salad plate, bowl, cup and saucer, and dessert bowl

Cups and saucers.

Dinner plate, salad plate, cup
and saucer (limited edition/
signature multiples/ Tom Strobel)

Imperial Ware

Imperial Ware is a medium-weight dinnerware line, whose marking doesn't contain any additional identifying information on it other than its name.

In a standard round shape its speckled and mottled pastel colors come in pink, yellow, blue and white. Other colors include a gray, a burgundy, and a dark green.

Imperial Ware Trademark

Imperial Trademark

Covered sugar bowls and creamers

Platter, creamer, and covered sugar bowl.

Dinner plate, salad plate, bowl, and cup and saucer.

Lucent

Lucent was a medium-weight melamine dinnerware line introduced in 1956 by the Lucent Corporation, New York. It was manufactured by J. & I. Block Corporation, New York, and the designers were Raymond Lowey Associates, who also designed the Lucent dinnerware retail packaging, a valise type box with a handle that opened up to display their product in a stylish way.

The main identifying features of Lucent pieces were its thin, sleek shape, the translucent quality of the melamine (hence its name), and its tall form due to heavier, round shaped bases that elevated the pieces.

Lucent came in solid colors of white, turquoise, pale yellow, and pink. There were three patterns available, and two of the patterns were Sun Petal and April in Paris.

Lucent Trademark

Divided serving bowl.

Plate "Sun Petal" pattern,
and saucer.

Plates, bowls, and
a cup and saucer.

Mallo-Ware

Mallo-Ware was a medium-weight melamine dinnerware manufactured by P. R. Mallory Plastics, Incorporated, Chicago, Illinois.

An identifying feature of Mallo-Ware was that each individual piece was marked on the bottom with a number and the name of the item (example: 55 saucer), as well as the usual identifying marks. Design features include their tab-handled bowls, and the solid, straight-edged handles of the creamer and the sugar bowl. Solid colors include yellow, gray, chartreuse, light green, beige, white, avocado, gold, and a patterned line named Moonglow.

Mallo-Belle was a dinnerware line that featured lighter pieces with trim lines, small bases on items, and a tapered look.

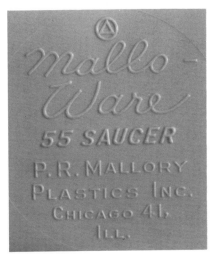

Mallo-Ware Trademark.

Mallo-Belle Trademark.

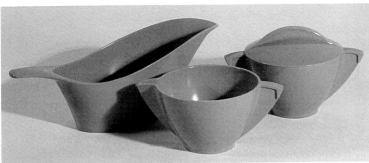

Gravy boat, creamer, and covered sugar bowl.

Dinner plate, bowl, and a cup and saucer.

A stack of cups and saucers.

61

Mar-crest

Mar-crest was a medium to lightweight dinnerware line from the Mar-crest Company in Chicago, Illinois.

There are two different styles of Mar-crest whose identifying features are seen particularly in the creamer, the sugar bowl, and the cup. In one style the creamer has a flat side-handle, the sugar bowl has two flat handles, and the cup handle is a triangular shape. In the other style the creamer has a standard finger hole handle, the sugar bowl is handleless, and the cup handles have the standard finger holes.

Colors came in pastel blue, yellow, pink, white, turquoise, and in an ordinary brown.

Mar-crest Trademark

Mar-crest Trademark

A platter and a divided serving bowl

Dinner plate, salad plate, soup bowl, cup and saucer, and dessert bowl.

Monte Carlo

Monte Carlo was a medium to lightweight dinnerware manufactured in New York, New York.

Monte Carlo's shapes nearly duplicate those of the pieces in the Aztec dinnerware line. In the collection there are mustard yellow colored pieces as shown below.

Monte Carlo Trademark

A bowl and a cup and saucer.

Prolon

Prolon was a diverse melamine dinnerware line manufactured by Prolon Plastics, a division of Prophylactic Brush Company, Florence, Massachusetts.

The early general dinnerware lines were solid colored, heavy melamine, and Prolon Ware in particular appears to have been used in institutional settings. The various Prolon styles and pattern names included Beverly, Cadence, Florence, Prolon Ware, Meladur, Hostess, World of Color, Designers, Bazaar, Artiste, Potpourri Vista, Grant Crest, Choraleer, Leonora, Ponderosa, Autumn Glory, and Radiance.

One of the most notable styles with special identifying features was called Florence, the namesake of the city where it was manufactured. This line was designed in 1953 by Irving Harper (of George Nelson Associates), and was inspired by, and based on traditional oriental lacquerware, with its trim, delicate lines, and overall gracefulness. These simple forms lent themselves to being easily reproduced in plastic molding processes. The characteristic elegance of Florence was not typical of most plastic dinnerware lines of the time, and it gave added dignity to the world of melamine tableware, and in fact the Florence line won the House Beautiful "Classic Award" in 1955.

The basic design of Florence pieces featured high-walled plates and platters, but with tapered edges, rimless bowls that gently flared upward, and a different cup-to-saucer relationship: the cup had a recessed bottom that fit on a saucer that had a pedestal center rather than the usual well center. It was believed that this connection produced a more stable cup-to-saucer relationship. (This feature was explored earlier in the Devine Ware melamine line designed by Jim Devine.)

Additionally, various pieces were intended for multiple use: plates could be platters; small bowls could be used for sugar or gravy and some of the bowls could also be used for flower arrangements or other displays.

The Florence line was available in the manufacturer's lacquer-like colors of Dawn (beige-gray), High Noon (mustard yellow), Sunset (red), and Midnight (black). Turquoise and white were added colors, as well as decal patterns. Unusual Florence pieces include a three-footed salad bowl, and a pair of salad servers.

Other Prolon styles had their own identifying features and colors. Prolon Ware featured bowls with both lipped rims and round rims, and cups with notched bottoms for uniform washing and drying purposes. Prolon Ware colors included burgundy, lime green, gray, dark green, turquoise, yellow, white, rust red, and an olive green. An uncommon piece of Prolon Ware was a compartmentalized food tray with matching cup in a mottled pea-green color.

Prolon Grant Crest was sold by W. T. Grant stores.

Prolon Ponderosa (for Ponderosa restaurants) had the word Ponderosa repeated in a pattern around the rim of its pieces. Another Prolon piece featured a creamer with an open-ended (or ponytail) handle.

Prolon Trademark

Prolon Florence Trademark

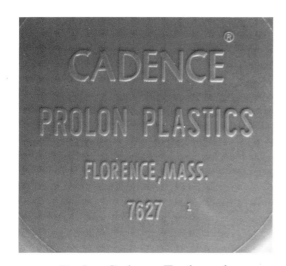

Prolon Cadence Trademark

Prolon Grant Crest
Trademark

Prolon Leonora Trademark

Prolon Ponderosa

Creamers, covered sugar bowls.

Dinner plate, bowl, and a
cup and saucer, "Beverly" pattern.

Cups and saucers.

Platter, serving bowl, covered
sugar bowl, creamer, and salt
and pepper, "Beverly" pattern.

Footed salad bowl.

Platters, divided serving bowl,
and a regular serving bowl.

Dinner plate, salad plate,
cup and saucer, and a bowl.

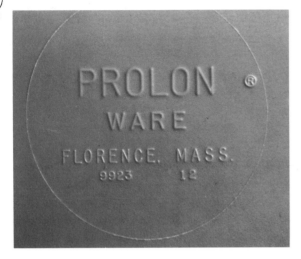

Prolon Ware Trademark

Dinner plate, salad plate, cup and saucer,
dessert bowl, and a soup bowl.

Cups and saucers.

Serving bowl, creamers, and covered sugar bowls.

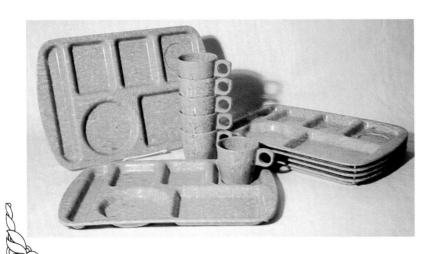

Compartmentalized food
trays with cups.

Restraware

Restraware was an institutional dinnerware line made by Applied Plastics Division of Keystone Brass Works, Erie, Pennsylvania. Another Restraware marking shows the Libbey Glass cursive L logo, and location as Toledo, Ohio.

Restraware Trademark

Royalon

Royalon was a medium weight dinnerware manufactured by Royalon Incorporated, Chicago, Illinois, a subsidiary of Royal China, Incorporated, Logansport, Indiana.

Royalon lines included Roymac, Royalon Windsor, Royalon Hallmark, Royalon World's Fair House, Royalon Candlelight, Windsor Melmac, and Brookpark by Royalon (Brookpark-Royalon).

The Royalon general dinnerware line solid color pieces were produced in white, turquoise, pink, purple, yellow, and beige, as well as patterned pieces, two of which are Aristocrat, and Violets.

The Windsor melamine was a well-known dinnerware line Royalon, and came in solid colors and patterned lines with names like San Marino, Romance, Jasmine, and Crescendo.

Royalon pieces had familiar smooth, rounded shapes, and in particular the covered sugar bowl featured an undulating round lid and handle. A Windsor accessory piece, the platter, had a unique squared-off oval shape.

You'll love
MELMAC®
Quality Melamine Dinnerware

Royalon
Pamphlet

You will be proud, too, of your very wise purchase because of its:

Quality . . . Individual brands equal or exceed quality standards established for your protection, endorsed by the industry and developed in cooperation with the U.S. Department of Commerce. Finally, an independent testing laboratory determines

adherence to MELMAC quality dinnerware standards.

Break-Resistance . . . Let children wash MELMAC. It resists chipping and cracking

Lasting Beauty . . . Patterns and colors are molded in. Standard household soaps and detergents can't wash them off, fade, or harm the surface.

Easy Care . . . Just wash MELMAC dinnerware with standard household soaps or detergents. It can be washed safely even in the very hot water of an automatic dishwasher. Do not scour with powders, pads or abrasives.

As with all fine dinnerware, staining from coffee or tea may result. To avoid this, rinse cups soon after use. Should

MELMAC is the registered trademark of American Cyanamid Company and may be used only with its authorization.

staining occur, it can be removed by rubbing briskly with a dishcloth and soap or by using one of these cleansers according to directions:

Boontonware®   **M-E Cleaner**

Dip-it®   **SNOWY® bleach**

For automatic dishwashers we suggest one of these detergents:

Cascade®   **Finish®**

Do not cook or warm foods in Melmac dinnerware or expose ware to flame . . . it might char.

Keep This Tag for
Ready Reference

ROYALON, INC.
Subsidiary of Royal China, Inc.
Logansport, Indiana

©American Cyanamid Company, 1963   Printed in U.S.A.

Royalon Trademark.

Royalon Roymac Trademark.

Creamers, and covered
sugar bowls.

Dinner plate, salad plate,
cup and saucer, and a bowl.

Serving bowl, covered sugar bowl, and creamer

Platter and serving bowl

Dinner plate, salad plate, soup bowl,
cup and saucer, and dessert bowl

Platter, covered sugar bowl, and creamer

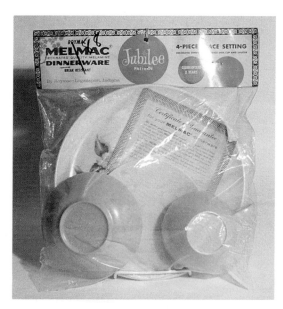

Four-piece starter set in original
packaging, "Jubilee" pattern

Royalon Windsor Trademark

Dinner plate, dessert bowl, and a cup and saucer

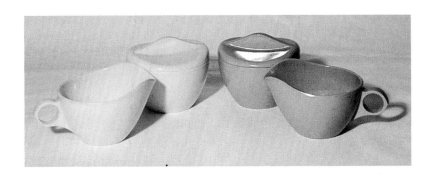

Creamers, and covered sugar bowls

Platter and a divided serving bowl

Russel Wright

The industrial designer Russel Wright, known for his home furnishing products, produced a number of designs for plastic dinnerware lines.

In 1945 Wright began working with American Cyanamid Corporation on melamine dinnerware prototypes. In 1949 the Meladur line was developed and designed by Wright in cooperation with the American Cyanide Company, New York, N.Y., and molded by the Plastic Dinnerware Division of the General American Transportation Company, Chicago, Illinois. Meladur was a heavy, hard, thick-walled dinnerware mostly designated for commercial restaurant or institutional use, and was made in pink, mint green, yellow, and blue. The pieces included familiar round shaped bowls, plates, and cups, as well as compartmentalized plates. Meladur items made between 1949 and 1953 have a Russel Wright signature in the marking.

Wright relinquished his design line to General American in 1953, and there are no signatures on items afterwards. Some of the prototypes by Wright for American Cyanamid continued to be made in the mid-1950's by Lapcor Plastics.

Residential was a full dinnerware line produced by Northern Industrial Chemical Company, Boston, Massachusetts, for domestic use, and was considered Russel Wright's most significant contribution to the plastic dinnerware industry receiving the Good Design Award from the Museum of Modern Art, New York, N.Y. in both 1953 and 1954. Residential design features included smooth, contoured, organic forms that allowed plates, bowls, cups, and platters to flow outward to include shaped handles, and provide unobtrusive molding seam lines called flash lines.

Residential pieces had heavy, solid-colored opaque bodies with a mottled effect made by overlapping two colors; the base coat color showed through an overcoat color. The original colors were Sea Mist, Grey, Lemon Ice, Copper Penny (brown with copper dust), and Black Velvet (black with aluminum dust). Added colors were salmon, white, and light blue.

Some of the more desirable Residential items include the fruit bowl, the covered onion soup bowl, the covered sugar bowl, the large tumblers, and the covered vegetable bowl.

Some pieces offered multiple use: the covers for the vegetable bowl and the onion soup bowl could serve as shallow bowls. Additional pieces were manufactured by Northern without Russel Wright's name in the marking, and included an early commercial line called Northernaire Ware.

In 1954 the Home Decorators line was introduced by Home Decorators, Incorporated, Newark, New York, with a design variant on the Residential shape, and producing the same items as in the Residential line. The colors were not clouded like the Residential line, but solid, and also patterned with a color overlay. Home Decorators came in white, blue, salmon, yellow, and pink. The pattern names were Bow Knot and Leaf.

In 1957 a line of dinnerware designed by Wright for the Ideal Toy Company was introduced. It was called Ideal Adult Kitchen Ware and was made of Fortiflex, a different synthetic material (polyethylene). This was a soft, flimsy type of material unlike the familiar hard melamine plastic. Ideal Ware was a type of refrigerator ware that was stackable, freezer proof, and included pieces with snap covers. It was referred to and advertised as a refrigerator-to-table product. It was available in manufacturer colors of mint, carnation, snow, blue mist, shrimp, and citron. Accessory pieces included covered leftover bowls, a juice decanter, a large water jug, and fork-and-spoon salad servers. Failing to meet long term consumer expectations, this line was soon discontinued.

In 1959 Wright's Flair line by Northern, Boston, Massachusetts, was introduced with a different shape from Residential and Home Decorators. The identifying feature of this line was the light, thin-walled design in solid colors and patterned pieces as well. The plates had small bases and rolled edges; cups also had small bases and a flared shape, with a small spur on the handle to form-fit the fingers holding it. The nearly translucent bodies of Flair pieces were available in five patterns: Golden Bouquet, Spring Garden, Woodland Rose, Arabesque, and Ming Lace which used actual leaves from the jade orchid tree that were imbedded and molded into the body of the pieces.

Flair

Russel Wright Flair Trademark

A plate and a cup and saucer

Plates, "Ming Lace" pattern

Great Northern

Great Northern Trademark

Dinner plate, cup and saucer.

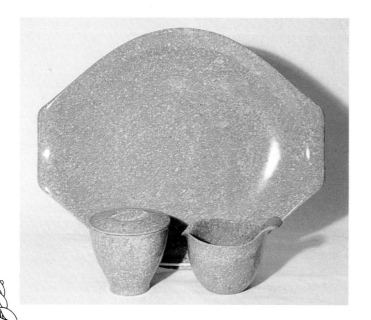

Platter, covered sugar bowl, and a creamer.

Home Decorators

Home Decorators Trademark

Divided serving bowl and a
covered onion soup bowl.

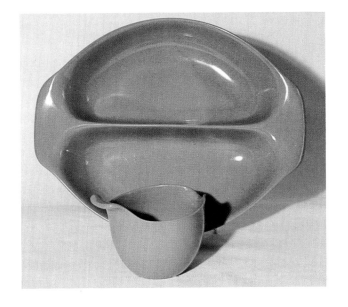

Divided serving bowl and creamer.

Bread and butter plate, dinner
plate, salad plate, soup bowl, cup
and saucer, and a dessert bowl.

Home Decorators continued . . .

Platter, divided serving bowl,
small tumbler, and creamer.

Dinner plate, salad plate,
soup bowl, cup and saucer,
and dessert bowl.

Idealware

Pitchers

Meladur

Meladur by General American Trademark.

Divided serving bowl and cup

Cups by Lapcor.

Residential

Residential Trademark.

Residential continued . . .

Platter and a divided
serving bowl.

Bread and butter plate, dinner plate,
salad plate, dessert bowl, small tumbler,
cup and saucer and a soup bowl.

Creamers and a sugar
bowl without a lid.

Spaulding

Spaulding and Spaulding Ware are a medium-weight dinnerware line from Spaulding Industries, Incorporated, manufactured by American Plastics Corporation, Chicago, Illinois.

Available in both solid and patterned pieces its colors included red, light blue, mustard yellow, turquoise, gray, pink, chocolate brown, in addition to a mottled variety.

An identifying feature of Spaulding is the unique cone-shaped knob handle on the cups, sugar bowls, and creamers. One of the markings on a Spaulding piece notes that it is "Artistically Designed".

Spaulding Trademark.

Spaulding Ware Trademark.

Platter and serving bowls.

Dinner plates and cups.

Platter, creamer, and covered sugar bowls.

Stetson

Stetson was a dinnerware line manufactured by Stetson Chemicals, Lincoln, Illinois, and Chicago, Illinois.

Stetson style names included Contour, Riviera, and Sun Valley. Sun Valley, a very popular style by Stetson, featured flat ended wing-like handles on the sugar bowls and creamers. Stetson's pastel colors included turquoise, pink, light green, yellow, and white. Additional colors in Sun Valley included a mottled orange and a butterscotch.

In the Riviera style one of the patterns was named Spring Violets. Curiously, one of the Stetson markings includes "For Lasting Beauty" in the mark.

Stetson Trademark.

Divided serving bowl,
cup and saucer.

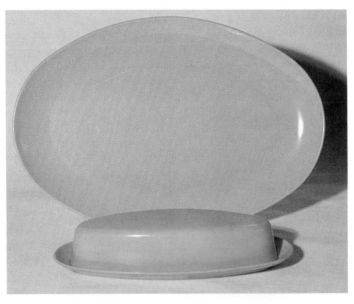

A platter and a covered butter dish.

Sun Valley Stetson Trademark.

Divided serving bowl, covered sugar
bowl, and a creamer.

Dinner plate, salad plate,
covered sugar bowl, and dessert bowl.

Texas Ware

Texas Ware is a varied heavyweight dinnerware manufactured by Plastics Manufacturing Company (PMC) in Dallas, Texas.

Dallas Ware, a partner to Texas Ware, is a more general commercial or institutional line of dinnerware, also manufactured by PMC or Plastics Manufacturing Company, Dallas, Texas, the makers of Texas Ware.

Other familiar Texas Ware lines included San Jacinto, Rio Vista, and El Capitan which are all regional Texas names. Sunberg-Ferar were designers with Texas Ware and in particular with the Rio Vista line in 1952, and the San Jacinto line in 1953. Manufacturer's colors for Rio Vista included Ebony Black, Bone White, Chinese Red, Stone Gray, and Sage Green. Other Rio Vista colors were turquoise, pink, and mustard yellow. San Jacinto manufacturer's colors in 1954 were Sea Green, Sage Green, Sandalwood (brown), Jonquil Yellow, Bone White, Dresden Blue, and Dusty Rose.

In 1957 PMC became the first plastic dinnerware manufacturer to mold color on color to produce duotone, or two-toned, items. Texas Ware's San Jacinto line won a Good Design Award from the Museum of Modern Art, New York, N.Y., for its Sandalwood on white, yellow on Dusty Rose, white on Sage Green, and gray on white items. Texas ware came in a variety of patterned styles: Shasta Daisy, Trend, Bon Vivant, Marco Polo, Avant Garde, Happenings, Classics, Epicure, Park Avenue, Westwood, Flourish, and Bouquet to name a few. The patterned styles named Angels and Autumn Leaves were designed by Phillip M. Brody.

Special pieces from Texas Ware include some dinner plates patterned with a portion of the United States flag's stars and stripes rendered in red, white, and blue; and a promotional advertising dinner plate with an invitation to dine from Southern Fried Chicken, Texas Style, at the Marriott Hotel in Chicago in January 1979.

Texas Ware Trademark.

Texas Ware Trademark.

Texas Ware San Jacinto Trademark.

Full page ad from a May 1955 magazine

Full page ad from an October 1956 magazine

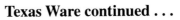

Dinner plate

Dinner plate, salad plate, dessert bowl,
cup and saucer, and soup bowl.

Dinner plate and salad plate,
"San Jacinto" design.

Serving bowl.

Creamers and
covered sugar bowls.

Dinner plate, salad plate, cup and
saucer, and a dessert bowl.

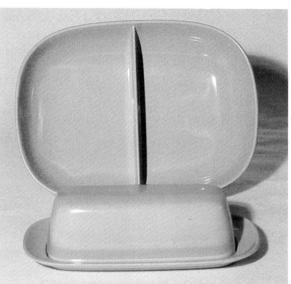

Divided serving bowl and a
covered butter dish.

U. S. Military

Cups and a tumbler.

Watertown

Watertown was a heavyweight plastic dinnerware line from the Watertown Manufacturing Company, Watertown, Connecticut. Watertown's styles included Lifetime Ware, Balmoral, Monterey, and Woodbine.

During World War II the United States Navy commissioned the Watertown Plastic Tableware Company to produce a dinnerware made of melamine, and through a U.S. Government purchase it was then utilized on Navy ships.

In 1947 Watertown Lifetime Ware was introduced, designed by Jon Hedu, and it became the first domestic consumer line available to the public.

Manufacturer's colors were Bermuda Coral, Sahara Sand, Caribbean Blue, Palisades Grey, Chartreuse, and Cocoa. Other colors included light blue, beige, black, red, yellow, and pink. Lifetime Ware was also available in a more translucent line in pale green, pink, blue, yellow, and white. An identifying design feature of Lifetime Ware is the downturned tab-handles on the covered sugar bowls.

Some of Watertown pattern names were Wheat, Country Gardens, Promenade, Puffs, and Cathay. More desirable accessory items in Watertown Lifetime Ware would include the water pitcher with lid, and the tumblers.

Monterey colors included yellow, brick red, gray, and pale blue. Watertown's Woodbine style, designed by Jon Hedu in 1952, introduced raised decorative patterns to plastic dinnerware manufacturing.

Watertown Ware Trademark.

Watertown Lifetime Ware Trademark.

Watertown Lifetime Ware Trademark.

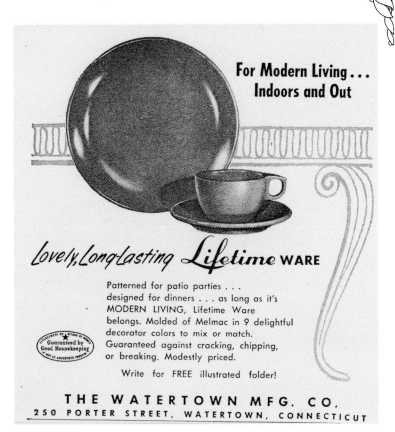

Advertisement for
Watertown Lifetime Ware.

Dinner plate, cup and saucer.

Water pitcher with lid.

Divided serving bowl
and a regular serving bowl.

Cups and saucers.

Tumblers.

Covered sugar bowls and creamers.

Dinner plate, salad plate,
cup and saucer, and a dessert bowl.

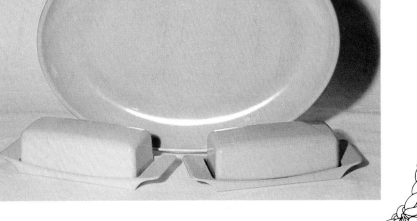

Platter and covered butter dishes.

Westinghouse

Westinghouse plastic dinnerware was manufactured by the Westinghouse Electric Corporation, Bridgeport, Connecticut, and included the Newport, Ovation, Darien, and Calais styles. The general dinnerware lines were a medium to heavyweight melamine and available in solid colors of turquoise, white, yellow, and pink, as well as patterned styles on white.

Westinghouse Ovation Trademark.

Westinghouse Newport Trademark.

Westinghouse Newport Trademark.

Dinner plate, salad plate, soup bowl, cup and saucer, and dessert bowl.

Platter, covered sugar bowl, creamer, and serving bowl.

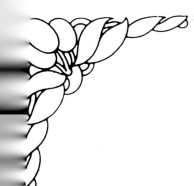

ADDITIONAL MELMAC DINNERWARE LINE
Names and Trademarks

Capac
Daileyware
deLux
King-Line
Meldale
Metro
Miramar
Nichols
Riviera Ware
Table to Terrace

de Lux

King-Line

Meldale

Riviera Ware

Table to Terrace

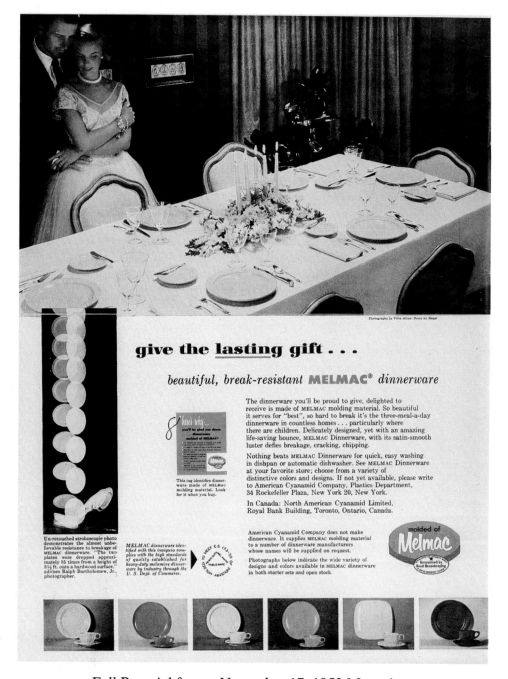

Full Page Ad from a November 17, 1952 Magazine.
(original size is 10 1/4" x 14")

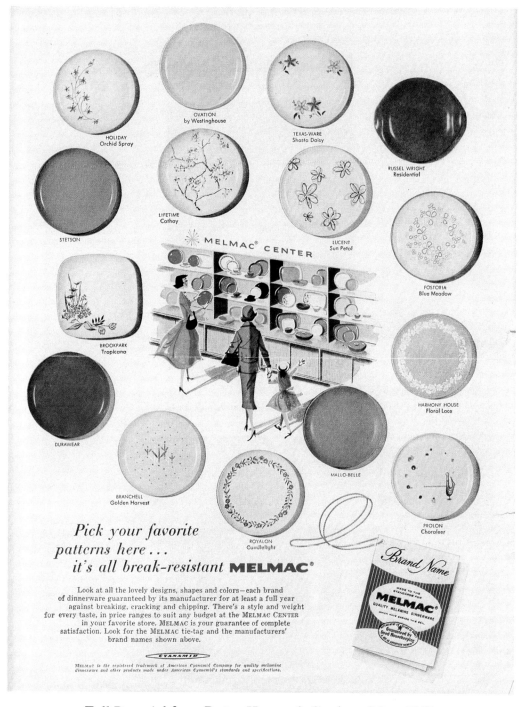

Full Page Ad from <u>Better Homes & Gardens</u>, May, 1958.
(original size is 9 1/4" x 13")

Full Page Ad from a May, 1962 Magazine.
(original size is 8" x 11")

Miscellaneous Melmac Advertising Pages

ANNOUNCING 1962 MELAMINE IN NEW BOOKLET: "INVITATION

"FLOWER BOX" by Brookpark, Inc. A Spring-fresh and radiant pattern with a beautiful hand-painted look. Perfect with pastels! A pattern that will always look bright and new.

"CARIBE" by Durawear from California Molded Products, Inc. Delicate orchid-like leaves on soft, muted white. Harmonious colors combine with others, easily and effectively.

"MING LACE LEAVES" by Northern Industrial Chemical Co. This Russel Wright design uses actual leaves of Jade Orchid Tree. Exotic! Looks stunning in a simple table arrangement.

"SPRING VIOLETS" by Stetson. A flurry of dainty violets in delicate shades of lavender. One of the loveliest of the new floral patterns! Will go well with accessories of any design.

Have you seen the new melamine? Won't you be surprised! Now in a greatly expanded range of stunning new colors and original new patterns, famous melamine dinnerware offers you new beauty for every dining occasion . . . every decor. Meanwhile, you *still* get the melamine bonus of amazing durability: melamine won't crack, chip or peel with everyday use. It's virtually unbreakable! *You must see the new melamine* (now in a wider range of prices, too)!

Full Page Ad from a May, 1962 Magazine.
(original size is 8" x 11")

Full Page Ad from a May, 1962 Magazine.
(original size is 8" x 11")

Full Page Ad from an October, 1966 Magazine.
(original size is 10" x 13 1/2")

Bibliography

The plastic dinnerware presented here appears through texts and advertisements in several general and trade periodicals of the time such as, <u>House and Garden</u>, <u>House Beautiful</u>, <u>Life</u>, <u>Look</u>, <u>Good Housekeeping</u>, <u>Industrial Design</u>, <u>Modern Plastics</u>, and <u>Everyday Art Quarterly</u>. Additional information can be obtained from catalogs of the period such as Montgomery Ward's, or other general merchandising catalogs.

Baird, Ronald J., <u>Industrial Plastics</u>. South Holland, Ill.,
    The Goodheart-Wilcox Co., Inc., 1971.

Di Noto, Andrea, <u>Art Plastic: Designed for Living</u>. New York, Abbeville Press, 1984.

Goldberg, Michael J., <u>Collectable Plastic Kitchenware and Dinnerware 1935-1965</u>.
    Schiffer Publishing Ltd., 1995.

Hines, Thomas, <u>Populuxe</u>. New York, Knopf, 1987.

Katz, Sylvia, <u>Plastics-Common Objects, Classic Design</u>. New York,
    Harry N. Abrams Inc., 1984.

Kerr, Ann, <u>The Collector's Encyclopedia of Russel Wright Design</u>.
    Collector Books, 1990.

Kerr, Ann, <u>Russel Wright Dinnerware-Designs for the American Table</u>.
    Collector Books, 1985.

McNulty, Lyndi, <u>A Price Guide to Plastic Collectables</u>. Radnor,
    Wallace-Homestead Book Co., 1987.

Pulos, Arthur J., <u>The American Design Adventure</u>. Cambridge, Mass.,
    The MIT Press, 1988.

Sparke, Penny (Editor), <u>The Plastics Age</u> (From Bakelite to Beanbags and Beyond).
    The Overlook Press, 1993

Wahlberg, Holly, <u>Everday Elegance: 1950s Plastics Design</u>.
    Schiffer Publishing Ltd., 1994

"Design in Plastics", D. A. Wallace, <u>Everyday Art Quarterly</u> No. 6: 3-4, 1947.

<u>Everyday Art Quarterly</u>, Walker Art Center, Minneapolis, No. 16, Fall 1950.

"Plastics on the Table", <u>Industrial Design</u>, Vol. 1, No. 2 (April 1954).

"What are Plastics", <u>Everyday Art Quarterly</u> No. 6: 1-3, 1947.

Price Guide

This price guide should be used as a general guide only. Supply and demand will determine the price in your area.

The prices stated are for mint condition only. Pieces with scratches, chips, cracks, and stains have no value.

The process of setting up the guide includes grouping together the lines that have similiar value. Some items are not available to all the different lines.

ABC, Air Flite, Apollo Ware, Aztec, Debonaire, Flite Lane, Imperial Ware, Mallo-Ware, Mar-Crest, Monte Carlo, Restraware, Rivieraware, Royalon, Royalon Windsor, Spaulding, Stetson, Texas Ware, and Westinghouse:

Bread plate	1.00-2.00
Butter dish	5.00-7.00
Cereal bowl	2.00-3.00
Creamer	1.00-2.00
Cup and Saucer	2.00-3.00
Dinner plate	2.00-3.00
Fruit bowl	1.00-2.00
Gravy boat	5.00-6.00
Salad plate	2.00-3.00
Serving bowl	4.00-5.00
Shakers	4.00-5.00
Soup bowl	3.00-4.00
Sugar bowl with lid	3.00-4.00
Tumbler 6 oz.	6.00-7.00
Tumbler 10 oz.	7.00-8.00

Boontoon, Branchell, Branchell Color-Flyte, Branchell Royale, Brookpark, Brookpark Arrowhead, Harmony House, Holiday, Prolon, and Watertown Lifetime Ware:

Bread plate	2.00-3.00
Bread tray	8.00-10.00
Butter dish	10.00-12.00
Cereal bowl	4.00-5.00
Compartment plate	10.00-12.00
Covered Casserole	20.00-25.00
Creamer	5.00-6.00
Cup and Saucer	3.00-4.00
Dinner plate	4.00-5.00
Divided vegetable bowl	8.00-10.00
Fruit bowl	3.00-4.00
Gravy boat	6.00-8.00
Jug with lid	20.00-25.00
Platter	8.00-10.00
Salad Plate	4.00-5.00
Salad tongs	12.00-15.00
Serving bowl	8.00-10.00
Shakers	6.00-8.00
Soup bowl with lid	5.00-6.00
Sugar bowl	6.00-8.00
Tidbit tray 2-tier	12.00-15.00
Tidbit tray 3-tier	15.00-18.00
Tumbler 6 oz.	10.00-12.00
Tumbler 10 oz.	12.00-15.00

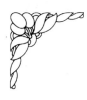
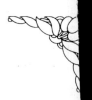

Fostoria and Lucent

Bread plate 3.00-4.00

Butter dish 15.00-18.00

Cereal bowl 7.00-9.00

Creamer 8.00-10.00

Cup and Saucer 8.00-12.00

Dinner plate 6.00-8.00

Platter 12.00-15.00

Relish tray 15.00-18.00

Serving bowl 15.00-18.00

Sugar bowl with lid 12.00-15.00

Russel Wright: Flair, Home Decorator, Idealware, Meladur, and Residential:

Bread plate 3.00-4.00

Butter dish 30.00-35.00

Cereal bowl 6.00-8.00

Chop plate 8.00-10.00

Compartment plate 10.00-12.00

Covered Casserole 30.00-35.00

Creamer 6.00-8.00

Cup and Saucer 8.00-10.00

Decanter, Juice 15.00-18.00

Dinner plate 6.00-7.00

Divided serving bowl 15.00-18.00

Freezing dish 12.00-15.00

Fruit bowl 12.00-15.00

Jug with lid 20.00-25.00

Leftover bowls 12.00-15.00

Lug Soup bowl 12.00-15.00

Onion soup bowl with lid 25.00-30.00

Oval vegetable bowl 15.00-18.00

Platter 15.00-18.00

Salad bowl 15.00-17.00

Salad plate 6.00-7.00

Salad servers 20.00-25.00

Salad tongs 12.00-15.00

Soup bowl 8.00-10.00

Sugar bowl with lid. 12.00-15.00

Tumbler 15.00-18.00